PUTTING GOD FIRST

By JIM BURNS

ILLUSTRATIONS BY RICK BUNDSCHUH

A workbook to be used alone as a study book on practical issues in your Christian faith, together with a friend or group of friends, or as a curriculum for Sunday school or youth group.

Books By Jim Burns:

LifeSources For Youth

Christian Life Series
Putting God First
Making Your Life Count
Living Your Life...As God Intended
Giving Yourself to God
Leader's Guide

Christian Growth Series
Commitment to Growth
Congratulations! You Are Gifted!
Getting It Together
Building Relationships...With God and Others
Leader's Guide

Handling Your Hormones—Trade size
Handling Your Hormones Growth Guide
Handling Your Hormones Leader's Guide
Getting In Touch With God (Youth Devotional)
Growth Unlimited—The 90-Day Experiment
(Youth Devotional)

HARVEST HOUSE PUBLISHERS
Eugene, Oregon 97402

DEDICATION

To Cathy, my best friend, co-worker, and loving wife.

Special thanks to Tic Long, Wayne Rice, and
Mike Yaconelli, three "crazies" and "geniuses"
who inspire me and challenge me.

PUTTING GOD FIRST
Copyright © 1982 by Harvest House Publishers
Eugene, Oregon 97402
ISBN 0-89081-366-3

TABLE OF CONTENTS

INTRODUCTION

It takes work to be a growing Christian! The people I've met who have a vibrant faith are willing to investigate what God's best is for their lives. They are men and women, guys and girls who realize that God's love, care, and concern for them is for every area of their lives, and they are willing to put their time, energy, and effort to allow God to work in their lives.

This workbook is designed to help you become a growing Christian. It was written to be as practical as possible. Hopefully, it will challenge you to not settle for second best in life, but strive to be all that God desires you to be.

You can use this workbook alone as a study book on practical issues in your Christian faith or you can use it together with a friend or group of friends. Some people might want to use it as a curriculum for Sunday school or youth group, and they will want to be sure and get the leader's edition as well.

Everywhere I go youth workers tell me they are looking for biblical, interesting, and practical workbooks to stimulate people to grow. My prayer is that this workbook will provide a stimulus to help you become all that you were meant to be in Christ.

"All flesh is like grass and all its glory like the flower of grass. The grass withers, and the flower falls, but the word of the Lord abides forever" (I Peter 1:24,25).

Your friend in Christ,

Jim Burns

1. Getting Our Priorities Straight

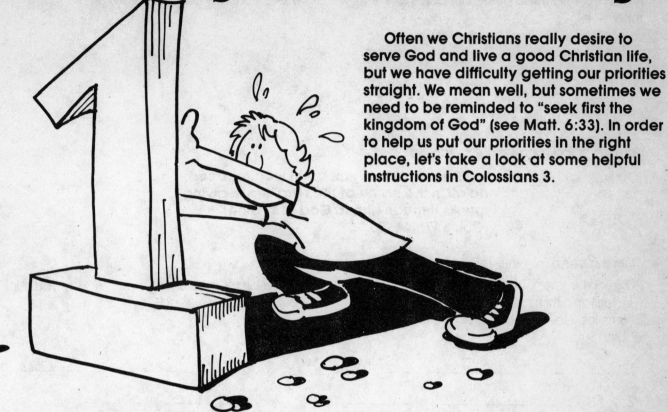

Often we Christians really desire to serve God and live a good Christian life, but we have difficulty getting our priorities straight. We mean well, but sometimes we need to be reminded to "seek first the kingdom of God" (see Matt. 6:33). In order to help us put our priorities in the right place, let's take a look at some helpful instructions in Colossians 3.

Read Colossians 3:1-17
Colossians 3:1-4.
As Christians, what are we to seek?

What does it mean to seek the things above?

How is Galatians 2:20 similar to Colossians 1:3?

Colossians 3:5-17.

In verses 5-9, Paul challenges us to put to death, or put away, "all these earthly things." He then goes on to list them.

Which earthly things do you have the most trouble with?

In verses 9,10, Paul challenges the believer to "put off the old nature with its practices, and put on the *new* nature." List the attributes of the new nature found in verses 12-17.

Put a mark by three of the attributes of the new nature that you truly desire to work on this week.

Here's a good memory verse for you:

"And whatever you do in word or deed, do all in the name of the Lord Jesus, giving thanks through Him to God the Father" (Col. 3:17, *NASB*).

With this verse in mind, let's take a priority inventory.

Put in order ten priorities in your life. (Understand that no one is perfect. Be honest.) Examples: devotional life; school; family; church, etc.

Now re-order your priorities in the way you think would best glorify God.

1. _____
2. _____
3. _____
4. _____
5. _____
6. _____
7. _____
8. _____
9. _____
10. _____

1. _____
2. _____
3. _____
4. _____
5. _____
6. _____
7. _____
8. _____
9. _____
10. _____

What steps will it take for you to live in a way that is consistent with your new priority list?

Here is a helpful suggestion.

Take a moment to look at the priorities you've put down on paper. List three of the priorities you would really like to work on soon. Then under each priority list three specific things you can do to get started. This week try to accomplish those goals.

Priority # 1   Priority # 2   Priority #3

For example, your priority is to improve your devotional life. You might list these goals: read through the New Testament; set aside 15 minutes every day; pray for family every day.

2. God's Ways Are Different Than Our Ways
(Developing a Proper Self-Image)

God loves you not for what you do but for who you are! You are His creation and He loves you unconditionally. The good news is this: He believes in you even when you don't believe in yourself.

Who are you in the eyes of God, according to John 1:12?
Remember: God's ways are different than our ways.

In order to gain acceptance in our society we usually must work hard to *earn* first team or a spot in the play or good grades. We have had to perform for almost everything we have ever gained. Yet this is simply not true about God's love. His ways are different than our ways. His love and acceptance come with no strings attached. You will never have to perform for God or earn your salvation through good works. (Read Ephesians 2:8,9.) God loves you because He created you.

Let's take a look at Psalm 139:13-18.

Read Psalm 139:13-18.

What was God's part in your creation?

4

After reading the psalm, do you think God cares about your physical features?

_____ Yes   _____ No   _____ Not sure

Explain your answer.

Does God care about your personality?

_____ Yes   _____ No   _____ Not sure

Explain your answer.

What did the psalmist say about the works of God in verse 14?

Many Christians severely criticize themselves for their personalities and physical attributes; but when we criticize ourselves we are, in a very real sense, criticizing the Lord God who created us. Ephesians 2:10 says:

For we are His workmanship, created in Christ Jesus for good works, which God prepared beforehand, that we should walk in them. *(NASB)*

In the Greek language (the New Testament was written in Greek), the word for workmanship can also be translated poetry. Just think. You are God's poetry!
What special abilities and qualities has God given to you that are above average, special or unique?

1. _____

2. _____

3. _____

4. _____

5. _____

Here's a little questionnaire to help you see just where you need help in your self image.

	Most of the time	Sometimes	Hardly ever
1 Are you a critical person?	_____	_____	_____
2 Are you a poor listener?	_____	_____	_____
3 Are you argumentative with friends or family?	_____	_____	_____
4 Would you consider yourself an angry person?	_____	_____	_____
5 Are you a forgiving person?	_____	_____	_____
6 Are you very impressed with titles, honors or degrees?	_____	_____	_____
7 Do you have difficulty accepting compliments from others?	_____	_____	_____
8 Do the people who know you consider you overly sensitive?	_____	_____	_____
9 Do you always have to be right?	_____	_____	_____
10 Are you a jealous person?	_____	_____	_____
11 Do you find it difficult to lose in games and sports or any other events?	_____		

Everyone has traits they need to work on. Using the questionnaire as a guide, list three areas in which you need the most improvement and three areas in which you are doing well.

What can you do to begin working on your more difficult areas?

This section consists of eight practical steps to developing a better self-image and becoming the person you were meant to be. Under each point plenty of room has been left to write your thoughts and comments about specific ways you can improve your self-image.

1. View yourself the way God views you.

> It is God himself who has made us what we are and given us new lives from Christ Jesus; and long ages ago he planned that we should spend these lives in helping others.
>
> **Ephesians 2:10** *(TLB)*

How does God view you?

What makes His love for you so special?

2. Accept God's forgiveness.

> If we confess our sins, He is faithful and righteous to forgive us our sins and to cleanse us from all unrighteousness.
>
> **I John 1:9** *(NASB)*

> I, yes I alone am he who blots away your sins for my own sake and will never think of them again.
>
> **Isaiah 43:25** *(TLB)*

What does God promise to do in I John 1:9 and Isaiah 43:25?

What makes this such good news?

Because God's ways are different than our ways, it is sometimes difficult to accept God's forgiveness. It is also hard to forgive ourselves even after God has forgiven us. What are a few areas in your life where you have confessed your sin to God, yet still have trouble forgiving yourself?

3. Become Others-Centered

For anyone who keeps his life for himself shall lose it; and anyone who loses his life for me shall find it again.
Matthew 16:25 *(TLB)*

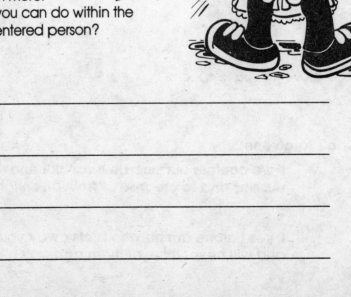

You've probably heard the phrase "lose yourself in the service of others." It is a fact that we can be much more fulfilled as we do good deeds for others. Instead of being an I-centered person, work at being an others-centered person and watch fulfillment come your way.

To become a more others-centered person you can: (1) do favors for friends or family; (2) give compliments; (3) be an available listener; and much, much more.

What are some specific things you can do within the next month to be a more others-centered person?

1. _____

2. _____

3. _____

4. _____

5. _____

4. Stay Healthy

Haven't you yet learned that your body is the home of the Holy Spirit God gave you, and that he lives within you? Your own body does not belong to you. For God has bought you with a great price. So use every part of your body to give glory back to God, because he owns it.

I Corinthians 6:19,20 *(TLB)*

An important factor in a proper self-image is taking care of your body. It is very important to watch what you eat, keep your body in good physical shape, get plenty of sleep and have enough time for relaxation.

How are you doing in each of these areas?

	Good	*O.K.*	*Needs work*
Eating habits	___	___	___
Staying in shape	___	___	___
Sleep	___	___	___
Relaxation	___	___	___

If any of these areas need work, write down a few specific goals to work on in the coming weeks.

5. Develop Meaningful Relationships

A true friend is always loyal.
Proverbs 17:17a *(TLB)*

We all need people who love us regardless. We all need intimacy, yet many people live life alone. James 5:16 says, "Confess your sins to one another, and pray for one another, so that you may be healed" *(NASB)*. Everyone needs a confidant. Who is your confidant?

List three people you would like to get closer to in the coming month.

1. _____

2. _____

3. _____

6. Avoid Negativism

This is the day which the Lord has made; Let us rejoice and be glad in it.
Psalm 118:24 *(NASB)*

To keep a proper self-image, avoid being negative. Negative, critical, argumentative and self-condemning people are unhappy people. Do you often find yourself taking on one or more of these negative characteristics?

What positive steps can you take to overcome these traits?

7. Growth Requires Effort

You will find me when you seek me, if you look for me in earnest.
Jeremiah 29:13 *(TLB)*

All of us at times want to grow by osmosis. Yet in order to grow in our Christian faith and self-image, we must discipline ourselves, pull up our shirt sleeves and get to work. What can you do that might require some effort on your part but that will definitely help your self-image?

Remember: If you don't *feel* like it, do it anyway. Your feelings will often come after your actions.

8. Set Specific Goals

We should make plans—counting on God to direct us.

Proverbs 16:9 *(TLB)*

Remember: He or she who aims at nothing, gets there every time.

Set realistic goals. Don't make your goals so high you'll never reach them, or so low you'll reach them too easily. Set goals that, with God's help, you can attain.

What are five specific goals you'd like to work on this year? Don't forget to commit these goals to God.

1. _____

2. _____

3. _____

4. _____

5. _____

3. Exploring Our Sexuality

   We live in a sexual, sensual society. Everywhere we look, from toothpaste commercials to billboards, advertisements to the local swimming pool, it seems that our society has gone "sex crazy." Let's get a rumor straight right away. Christians are tempted just like anyone else when it comes to sexuality and promiscuity. At times churches have done a poor job of communicating about the sexual life of Christian young people. In fact, sometimes the church has done more harm than good. Let's take a look at sexuality from a Christian viewpoint.

I. Why does sex have such an influence in our lives?

1. We live in a sexual society. (Our lives are bombarded from every direction with messages to live a more sexual life.)

2. Sex is mysterious! Every normal human being is curious about sexuality.

II. How does God view sex? (Is He a great killjoy concerning sex?)

Read Genesis 2:18-25.

Who created our sex lives?

Read Genesis 1:26-31.

What did God ask the first man and woman to do in Genesis 1:28?

In Genesis 1:31, what words did God use to describe His creation?

Do you think these sections of Scripture apply to our sexual lives?

_____ yes   _____ no

Of course they do! God created sex and He looks at sex as a very good thing. God takes sex seriously. He sees it as sacred and important. Let's read on to see more about how He views our sexuality.

Read Matthew 19:4-6.

What word or words (depending on the version of Scripture you use) does Jesus use to describe when a man and woman are "joined together" in verse 5?

What is the significance of these words of Jesus?

What else does the Bible say about our sexuality? Read the following Scriptures and restate their messages in your own words.

1. I Thessalonians 4:3-5

2. Exodus 20:14

3. I Corinthians 6:18

Why do you think God's best for us is to refrain from sexual intercourse until we are married?

No temptation has overtaken you but such as is common to man. **God is faithful, who will not allow you to be tempted beyond what you are able; but with the temptation will provide the way of escape also, that you may be able to endure it.**
I Corinthians 10:13 *(NASB,* **emphasis added)**

A few thoughts on forgiveness.

Christians can fall in the area of sexual temptation just as in other areas. It is important to note the following facts:

1. As we confess our sin, God forgives us.

If we confess our sins, He is faithful and righteous to forgive us our sins and to cleanse us from all unrighteousness.

I John 1:9 *(NASB)*

2. We must accept God's forgiveness.
As God forgives us, it is important that we then forgive ourselves. Forgiveness is something we never deserve, but God forgives us because He loves us unconditionally.

3. Repent.
In other words, stop doing what we are doing, at all costs. Continued sin blocks our relationship with Jesus.

Take some time right now to pray about your sex and dating life. Invite our loving Lord to be a part of that part of your life as well as other parts. God is not the great killjoy when it comes to sex. He loves you and He simply wants the very best for you.

Every normal, red-blooded young person will most likely, at one time or another, come in contact with sexual temptation. As Christians, we know what is best for us, but it is still a struggle. The temptation the world places on us is very great. Without God's help, let's face it, we're in trouble! However, we can take some **positive steps to overcome sexual temptation.**

Here are a few of those steps.

1. Talk about the problem with your boyfriend or girlfriend.
If you do not feel comfortable enough to talk with him or her about your problem, you are definitely going too far and need to seriously consider where your relationship is going to take you.

2. Set standards.
As you get to know your special friend, talk about the standards you would like to set in your relationship. Don't be afraid your friend will think you are a prude. He or she will respect you; if not, is the relationship worth it? Set your standards *before* you find yourself in the wrong place at the wrong time.

3. Plan dates that are fun and enjoyable.
One of the best ways to overcome sexual temptation is to stay away from "parking spots." Plan dates that allow you to have a lot of fun, with time for good communication.

4. Pray together.

Many Christians find it a great help to pray before a date. This puts the date in a proper perspective and often will remind both of you that, in a very real sense, the Lord goes with you on your dates.

5. Break up.

If you are unable to overcome sexual temptation, it would be wise to break up. At the time you might not feel that there are other "fish in the sea," but there are, and probably some who are better for you. Also, a breakup doesn't mean forever. Perhaps both of you need some time to redirect your thoughts; at another point in your life you may be able to get back together.

6. Let God be a part of your dating life.

As in all other areas of life, we need the Lord's help and guidance. Invite God on your dates. Let Him lead you and direct you to the right people to date. And memorize I Corinthians 10:13.

4. Walking in the Spirit

Do you ever feel that your Christian faith is dry? Do you ever ask the question, "Why can't I be living an abundant Christian life?"

You've heard people talk about the "power to live the Christian life" but you seem to run out of gas. If you've ever asked these questions or felt this way, then this Bible study is for you.

Many people have asked Christ to come into their lives but have never understood the role of the Holy Spirit (the third part of God) in helping them live a Spirit-filled, Christ-centered life. This section will teach us to take a walk in the Spirit.

I. Who is the Holy Spirit and why did He come?

Acts 1:8 _____

Matthew 28:19 _____

John 16:13,14 _____

John 14:16,17 _____

II.. **What does the Holy Spirit do to and for a person when he or she becomes a Christian?**

John 3:5

I Corinthians 3:16

Ephesians 4:30

I Corinthians 12:13

II Corinthians 5:5

III. **Read Galatians 5:16-26. Now paraphrase this section in your own words.**

What are the results of walking in the Spirit, according to Galatians 5:23,24?

What are the works of the flesh found in Galatians 5:19-21?

GAG!

WORKS OF THE FLESH

Let's take a "Fruit of the Spirit" inventory.

Below is a list of each Fruit of the Spirit. Mark in the appropriate box how you feel you are doing in each area.

	Good	Average	Poor
Love	☐	☐	☐
Joy	☐	☐	☐
Peace	☐	☐	☐
Patience	☐	☐	☐
Kindness	☐	☐	☐
Goodness	☐	☐	☐
Faithfulness	☐	☐	☐
Gentleness	☐	☐	☐
Self-control	☐	☐	☐

This week, ask God to help you in the areas in which you need a lot of work.

IV. What is the Christian commanded to do in Ephesians 5:18?

Ephesians 5:18 commands us to "be filled with the Spirit." In the Greek (the language the New Testament was written in), "be filled" actually means to "keep on being filled constantly and continually." It is a daily act of letting go of our self-centered ways, our problems and hassles, and allowing God to take control of every situation.

How can we be filled or empowered by the Holy Spirit? Read Matthew 7:7-11.

In review

The Holy Spirit is a part of the *Triune God.* (Matt. 28:19)

The Holy Spirit gives us the *power* to witness. (Acts 1:8)

The Holy Spirit will *guide* believers in all things. (John 16:13)

The Holy Spirit *glorifies* Jesus Christ. (John 16:14)

The Holy Spirit is our *Counselor (RSV), Comforter (TLB), Helper (NASB).* John 14:16,17.

Many Christians are simply not aware of the work of the Holy Spirit in our lives. This section should help you see the great importance of allowing the Holy Spirit to work in your life in order to live your Christian life to the fullest possible extent.

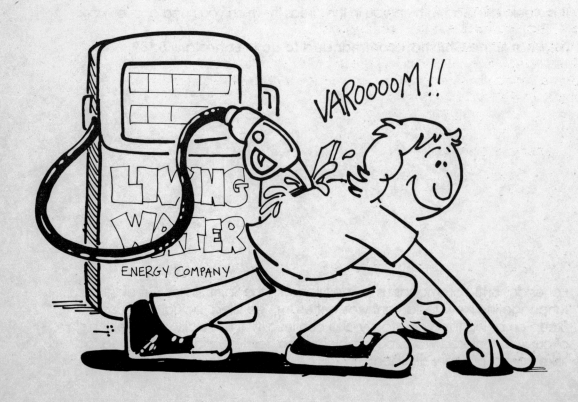

5. Thank Therapy ♪♫♪

Over and over again the Scripture tells us to be a thankful people. No one can read the Psalms (songs of the Hebrew people) and not be affected by the theme of thankfulness running through the pages of that great hymnal.

As you look around you, think for a moment: who are the happy and fulfilled people you know? Most likely these people are also thankful and grateful people. Thankfulness is a key which can help dispel your depressive emotions.

Where do you fit in on the thankfulness scale? Are you a grumbler and complainer, or do you consider yourself a thankful and grateful person? Mark an X where you fit in on this scale.

X ————————————————|————————————————— X
grumbler/complainer   grateful/thankful

Let's take a look at what a few of the Psalms have to say about thankfulness.
Psalm 7:17 Why is the Psalmist thankful?

Psalm 50:4 What kind of sacrifice does the Psalmist offer to God?

Psalm 92:1-4 Why is it good to give thanks to the Lord?

Psalm 100:1-5 What are the key points in this short but powerful Psalm?

Psalm 107:1;
Psalm 136:1 Why should we give thanks to the Lord?

Psalm 138:1 How should we give thanks to the Lord?

Christians have much to be thankful for. Yet we all struggle at times with being ungrateful servants in our Father's house. Here are three facts that will help us to be more thankful people.

Fact One: Thankfulness is an attitude.

In I Thessalonians 5:18 Paul tells us what God's will is for our lives. Read I Thessalonians 5:18. When I read that I should be thankful in *all* situations, I:

__a) believe it, but it is hard to put into practice.

__b) think it is impossible to do.

__c) don't understand exactly what Paul is trying to say in this verse.

__d) wish I could develop that trait in my life.

__e) feel it is good to do sometimes and not so good to do at other times.

Notice that the Scripture does not say to be thankful *for* all situations, it says to be thankful *in* all situations. How ridiculous to be thankful for a negative problem! But when we are challenged to be thankful *in* all circumstances, it is much easier to see that even in difficult times there are reasons to be thankful.

At one time or another everyone begins to feel sorry for himself or herself. At times we feel like we got the "short end of the stick." Yet it is important for us to have an attitude of thankfulness. No matter who you are or what troubles have come your way, you have a great many reasons to be thankful.

Sometimes we need to hear the old Indian proverb that says, "I complained because I had no shoes until I met a man who had no feet."

Fact two: You need to make thankfulness a habit in your life.

We all have good habits and bad habits. Often we focus on our bad habits; yet as Christians we need to work on developing good habits. If you develop the good habit of placing thankfulness in your heart on a daily basis, your life will be better in every way.

"Thank Therapy" is a formula that takes seriously Paul's command to "be thankful in all situations." Thank therapy is simply writing on paper 20 reasons why you are thankful. At first glance 20 reasons sounds like a lot, but as you begin writing you'll find that it is simple to list these reasons and you'll see how helpful it is to be reminded of God's blessings in your life. As you become consciously aware of why you are thankful to God for what He has already done for you, great things will begin to develop in your spirit.

Let's practice Thank Therapy!

List 20 things for which you are thankful. (Example: Jesus Christ; family; your church; eyeglasses; health; weather; etc.)

1. _____
2. _____
3. _____
4. _____
5. _____
6. _____
7. _____
8. _____
9. _____
10. _____
11. _____
12. _____
13. _____
14. _____
15. _____
16. _____
17. _____
18. _____
19. _____
20. _____

Review this list regularly, and add to it whenever you can.

Fact three: Jesus Christ paid the ultimate sacrifice for our sin; because of this we can be thankful.

What is the good news found in Romans 5:8?

How can this fact help you be thankful even when things are getting difficult?

23

6. The Cost of Commitment

A deeper commitment to Jesus means that you give up your will to the will of God. A deeper commitment means being willing to go anywhere and do anything for Jesus Christ. A deeper commitment to Jesus Christ involves surrender and obedience to your Lord. A deeper commitment means being in submission to the will of God. A deeper commitment means living your life in Christ, through Christ, because of Christ and not on your own but by the power of the Holy Spirit.

The Apostle Paul put it this way in Galatians 2:20: "I have been crucified with Christ; and it is no longer I who live, but Christ lives in me; and the life which I now live in the flesh I live by faith in the Son of God, who loved me and delivered Himself up for me" (NASB).

And as He was setting out on a journey, a man ran up to Him and knelt before Him, and began asking Him, "Good Teacher, what shall I do to inherit eternal life?" And Jesus said to him, "Why do you call Me good? No one is good except God alone. You know the commandments, 'Do not murder, Do not commit adultery, Do not steal, Do not bear false witness, Do not defraud, Honor your father and mother.'" And he said to Him, "Teacher, I have kept all these things from my youth up." And looking at him, Jesus felt a love for him and said to him, "One thing you lack: go and sell all you possess, and give to the poor, and you shall have treasure in heaven; and come, follow Me." But at these words his face fell, and he went away grieved, for he was one who owned much property. (Mark 10:17-22, NASB).

1. What will it cost to follow Jesus?

2. Riches may or may not be your problem. However, if Jesus were saying to you, "You lack one thing," how do you think He would complete the sentence?

24

Let's look at a few verses on commitment.

> Trust in the Lord with all your heart,
>   and do not rely on your own insight.
> In all your ways acknowledge him,
>   and he will make straight your paths.
> > Proverbs 3:5,6 *(RSV)*

> Commit your way to the Lord;
>   trust in him, and he will act.
> > Psalm 37:5 *(RSV)*

> Then Jesus told his disciples, "If any man would come after me, let him deny himself and take up his cross and follow me."
> > Matthew 16:24 *(RSV)*

According to Proverbs 3:5,6, what will happen when we trust in the Lord with all our heart, do not rely on our own understanding and in all our ways acknowledge Him?

According to Psalm 37:5, what is the result of committing our way to the Lord?

What do you think it means in Matthew 16:24 to deny yourself, take up your cross and follow Jesus?

25

The following is a letter from a communist student who is breaking his engagement with his fiancee. While reading this letter, think how it compares to our commitment and dedication to Jesus Christ.

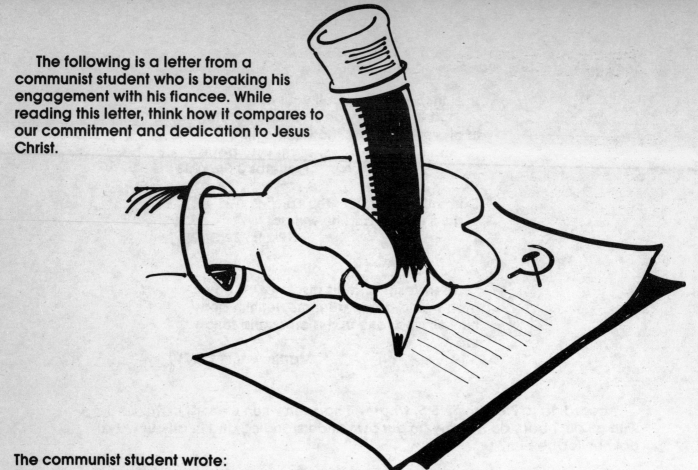

The communist student wrote:

"We communists have a high casualty rate. We are the ones who get shot and hung and ridiculed and fired from our jobs and in every other way made as uncomfortable as possible. A certain percentage of us get killed or imprisoned. We live in virtual poverty. We turn back to the party every penny we make above what is absolutely necessary to keep us alive. We communists do not have the time or the money for many movies, or concerts, or T-bone steaks, or decent homes, or new cars. We have been described as fanatics. We are fanatics. Our lives are dominated by one great overshadowing factor: The struggle for world communism. We communists have a philosophy of life which no amount of money can buy. We have a cause to fight for, a definite purpose in life. We subordinate our petty personal selves into great movement of humanity; and if our personal lives seem hard or our egos appear to suffer through subordination to the party, then we are adequately compensated by the thought that each of us in his small way is contributing to something new and true and better for mankind. There is one thing in which I am in dead earnest about, and that is the communist cause. It is my life, my business, my religion, my hobby, my sweetheart, my wife, and my mistress, my breath and meat. I work at it in the daytime and dream of it at night. Its hold on me grows, not lessens, as time goes on; therefore, I cannot carry on a friendship, a love affair, or even a conversation without relating it to this force which both drives and guides my life. I evaluate people, books, ideas, and actions according to how they affect the communist cause, and by their attitude toward it. I've already been in jail because of my ideals, and if necessary, I'm ready to go before a firing squad."[1]

What are your thoughts about this letter? Do you think it relates in any way to our Christian life?

Read Matthew 14:22-33.

How would you have reacted if you were in the boat with the disciples and you saw what looked like a ghost walking on the water?

If you had been Peter and Jesus said, "Come," how would you have felt? Do you think you would have stepped out into the water? Why?

What did Peter have to do in order not to sink? (See v. 30.)

Commitment can be costly and risky. Peter had to step out of the boat to see if it was really Jesus. He had to obey the voice of Jesus. It was risky, but he learned a great lesson.

Is Jesus calling you to commit a certain part of your life to Him? (Examples: relationships with friends or family, use of money, peer pressure, self-discipline.)

How will you respond to this call?

This year my commitment to Jesus Christ has been:

_____ Growing in leaps and bounds

_____ Stagnant

_____ Not growing at all

_____ Growing steadily

_____ Up and down

_____ _____

Complete this sentence:
What I need to do to have a deeper commitment to Jesus Christ this year is . . .

Footnote
1. Bill Bright, *Revolution Now* (San Bernardino, California: Campus Crusade for Christ), pp. 186,187.

7. The Call to Servanthood

FROG KISSIN'

Ever feel like a frog? Frogs feel slow, low, ugly, puffy, drooped, pooped. I know. One told me. The frog feeling comes when you want to be bright but feel dumb, when you want to share but are selfish, when you want to be thankful but feel resentment, when you want to be great but are small, when you want to care but are indifferent.

Yes, at one time or another each of us has found himself on a lily pad floating down the great river of life. Frightened and disgusted, we are too froggish to budge. Once upon a time there was a frog. But he really wasn't a frog. He was a prince who looked and felt like a frog. A wicked witch had cast a spell on him. Only the kiss of a beautiful maiden could save him. But since when do cute chicks kiss frogs? So there he sat, unkissed prince in frog form. But miracles happen. One day a beautiful maiden grabbed him up and gave him a big smack. Crash! Boom! Zap!! There he was, a handsome prince. And you know the rest. They lived happily ever after. SO WHAT IS THE TASK OF THE CHURCH? TO KISS FROGS, OF COURSE.[1]

What do you see is the significance in this "frog kissin'" story?

How can it relate to your circumstances at your church?

Now before the feast of the Passover, when Jesus knew that his hour had come to depart out of this world to the Father, having loved his own who were in the world, he loved them to the end. And during supper, when the devil had already put it into the heart of Judas Iscariot, Simon's son, to betray him, Jesus, knowing that the Father had given all things into his hands, and that he had come from God and was going to God, rose from supper, laid aside his garments, and girded himself with a towel. Then he poured water into a basin, and began to wash the disciples' feet, and to wipe them with the towel with which he was girded. He came to Simon Peter; and Peter said to him, "Lord, do you wash my feet?" Jesus answered him, "What I am doing you do not know now, but afterward you will understand." Peter said to him, "You shall never wash my feet." Jesus answered him, "If I do not wash you, you have no part in me." Simon Peter said to him, "Lord, not my feet only but also my hands and my head!" Jesus said to him, "He who has bathed does not need to wash, except for his feet, but he is clean all over; and you are clean, but not all of you." For he knew who was to betray him; that was why he said, "You are not all clean."

When he had washed their feet, and taken his garments, and resumed his place, he said to them, "Do you know what I have done to you? You call me Teacher and Lord; and you are right, for so I am. If I then, your Lord and Teacher, have washed your feet, you also ought to wash one another's feet. For I have given you an example, that you also should do as I have done to you. Truly, truly, I say to you, a servant is not greater than his master; nor is he who is sent greater than he who sent him. If you know these things, blessed are you if you do them. I am not speaking of you all; I know whom I have chosen; it is that the scripture may be fulfilled, 'He who ate my bread has lifted his heel against me.' I tell you this now, before it takes place, that when it does take place you may believe that I am he. Truly, truly I say to you, he who receives any one whom I send receives me; and he who receives me receives him who sent me." John 13:1-20 *(RSV)*

Why do you think Jesus washed His disciples' feet?

What lesson did Peter learn from his encounter with Jesus?

What is the path of blessing according to this Scripture: "If you know these things, blessed are you if you do them" (John 13:17, *RSV*)?

Very often we think of the preacher on Sunday morning as the minister and the congregation as non-ministers. That is just not true. **We who call ourselves Christians are all ministers.** The Greek word for minister also means to serve. It is the role and lifestyle of every Christian to be a servant . . . to be others-centered.

Our role and lifestyle in this world is to be a lover! In a world where people are hurting and suffering from lack of meaningful relationships we are called to love them, kiss frogs and make them into beautiful maidens or handsome princes. Karl Menninger, a famous psychiatrist, says that 90% of all the people who come to him for help are seeking love. He says, "Love is the medicine of the world."

There are two types of people in the world—I-centered, me-first people and others-centered people. Which kind of a person are you? Place a mark on the continuum.

X ———————————————————————————— X
SELF-CENTERED   OTHERS-CENTERED

Here's an interesting statement:

> **"If . . . a person seeks not to receive love, but rather to give it, he or she will become loveable and will most certainly be loved in the end."[2]**

That statement is a paradox! We all want to be loved; however, instead of seeking to be loved, we need to go out and love, care and serve others. In doing this we become loveable and we experience the important joy of being loved by others.
Read the statement again and put it into your own words:

Here are four points about being others-centered:

1. **Actions speak louder than words!**
   "Little children, let us not love in word or speech but in deed and in truth" (I John 3:18, *RSV*).
   What actions could you do to be a more others-centered person? (List at least five.) Be as specific as possible.

2. **Treat others as royalty.**

"Love one another with brotherly affection;
outdo one another in showing honor"
(Romans 12:10, *RSV*).

What specifically can you do to treat others as royalty?

Name three people God is putting on your heart to treat
in a special way. What do you plan to do to treat them as
royalty?

Name   **What You Plan to Do**

_____   _____

_____   _____

_____   _____

3. **Lose yourself in the service of others.**

"For whoever would save his life will
lose it; and whoever loses his life for my
sake, he will save it" (Luke 9:24, *RSV*).

Try an experiment: Think of the happiest and most fulfilled person you know. The odds are this person you are thinking of is the most caring, unselfish, serving person you know also. You can lose your own problems as you serve and help others.

Fill in this sentence: What would help me most to become a more others-centered person is—

_____

_____

4. You are the only Jesus somebody knows.

When you ask Jesus to come into your life, He promises to take up residence in your life. You become a representative of Jesus to others. Since many people never go to church, read the Bible or pray, the only way they will ever discover the forgiving and loving power of Jesus is by **seeing** Him in your life. That's why you are the only Jesus somebody knows!

Complete this sentence:
When I hear the phrase, "You are the only Jesus somebody knows" I feel:

A. Challenged

B. Overwhelmed

C. Scared

D. Excited that He lives in me

E. I've got a long way to go

F. Hopeful

Complete this sentence:
If there is one thing this Bible study on servanthood has taught me it is:

Here's an Inspiring Story . . .

There was a soldier who was wounded in battle. The padre crept out and did what he could for him. He stayed with him when the remainder of the troops retreated. In the heat of the day he gave him water from his own waterbottle, while he himself remained parched with thirst. In the night, when the chill frost came down, he covered the wounded man with his own coat, and finally wrapped him up in even more of his own clothes to save him from the cold. In the end the wounded man looked up at the padre. "Padre," he said, "you're a Christian?" "I try to be," said the padre. "Then," said the wounded man, "if Christianity makes a man do for another man what you have done for me, tell me about it, because I want it." Christianity in action moved him to envy a faith which could produce a life like that.[3]

This is the type of Christian we all need to be striving to be. The dying man saw Jesus in the actions of the padre. May God use you someday in a similar manner.

Footnotes
1. Wes Seeliger, church bulletin quoted in Bruce Larson, *Ask Me to Dance* (Waco, Texas: Word, Inc., 1972), pp. 11,12.
2. John Powell, *Why Am I Afraid to Love?* (Niles, Illinois: Argus Communications, 1972), p. 105.
3. William Barclay, *The Letter to the Romans, The Daily Study Bible Series,* Rev. Ed. (Philadelphia, Pennsylvania: 1975), p. 148.

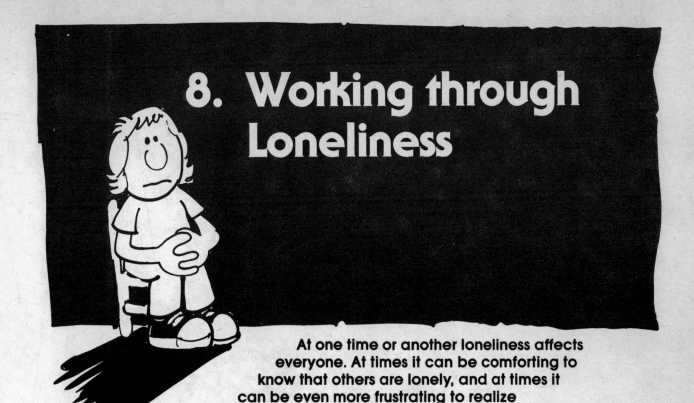

8. Working through Loneliness

At one time or another loneliness affects everyone. At times it can be comforting to know that others are lonely, and at times it can be even more frustrating to realize that almost everyone gets lonely and yet few know what to do about that loneliness.

In any group of people you are involved with, there are an incredible number of deep problems, hurts and frustrations; and loneliness is perhaps at the top of the list.

Billy Graham gave a talk on loneliness at one of his crusades some time ago. The talk was televised all over the world. He reports that in response to this one talk he received more mail than from any other single talk he had ever given. Why? Because basically, the world is lonely. And the news gets worse! Loneliness can cripple your personality, your self-image, your lifestyle and your relationship with God. Some have concluded that the decade of the 80's might one day be summed up as "the decade of loneliness."

How do we deal with our loneliness? There is hope. God can and does help us with our loneliness. He doesn't promise to wipe out our loneliness forever, but He does promise to walk with us through the valley of the shadow (see Ps. 23:4). Here are four suggestions to help deal with loneliness, and some ideas to help you get through the times of loneliness.

1. **Risk developing special friendships.**
   Who would you like to become more intimate with in your group or family? List three or four names.

   _____

   _____

   _____

   _____

Most likely these people would also like to develop a better friendship with you. Remember, it takes time to develop good relationships.

What can you do with each individual on your list within the next two weeks to strengthen the relationship? (Examples: lunch together, shopping, bike riding.)

Remember, it takes risk to develop special friendships, but the risk is worth it when you have a friend to help you through your loneliness. No doubt you will help your friend through his or her loneliness as well.

2. Be creative when you are lonely.

When you feel the lonely bug come over you, be creative: go for a walk, pray, read a good book, write a letter, read the Bible (Psalms and Proverbs can be especially helpful), treat yourself to a dessert, call a friend and do something special together.

Make a list of special things you like to do. Write down at least ten.

1. _____
2. _____
3. _____
4. _____
5. _____
6. _____
7. _____
8. _____
9. _____
10. _____

Keep this list handy. Next time you feel lonely read through this list and do one or more of the things you have suggested.

3. Be others-centered.

We live in a me-first, I-centered society. Yet me-first, I-centered people are lonely. What can you do to be a more others-centered person? List at least five special service-oriented things you can do. Be as specific as possible. (For example, bake cookies for Grandma; mow the lawn this afternoon; write an encouraging note today.)

1. _____

2. _____

3. _____

4. _____

5. _____

4. Commit your loneliness to God.

Jesus said, "Come to Me, all who are weary and heavy laden, and I will give you rest. Take My yoke upon you, and learn from Me, for I am gentle and humble in heart; and you shall find rest for your souls." (Matt. 11:28,29, *NASB*.) God wants us to give our burdens to Him. It's a fact! He will comfort us!

What are a few burdens that you need to take off your shoulders and place on the strong, sturdy shoulders of our Lord?

Take a few moments to read Psalm 23.

Why is this Psalm so comforting to those who are lonely?

Where in this Psalm do we receive *hope*?

9. A Lifestyle of Love
(Helps for Sharing your Faith)

It is only natural that as you grow in your Christian faith you will want to share the good news of Jesus Christ with your friends and loved ones. At the same time, many Christians feel timid about sharing spiritual things. We're afraid of being put down or being rejected. Sometimes we're even afraid we might embarrass God. So many of us simply pray for our non-Christian friends and family, but seldom talk with them about the Lord.

Let's get two misconceptions cleared up right away.

1. Witnessing is *not* a certain packaged formula to memorize and spout off word for word like a robot. (There are, however, certain witnessing helps and verses you will want to know well—but don't treat anyone like a machine.) **Witnessing is meeting people where they are, and treating them as special people, the way God would treat them.**

2. You don't have to be **perfect** to witness. The best witnessing takes place when you are open about your hurts, joys and even doubts, yet share what God has done for you in Jesus Christ. People will not be turned off by your weakness and vulnerability. They will be turned off if they can't identify with Mr. and Miss Perfection.

Have you ever heard the phrase, "Jesus is the answer"? Most likely you have. As Christians we know that statement to be true. Yet the unbeliever has not even asked the question. Sometimes we are giving the answer to an unasked question. Lloyd Ogilvie has said, "We ought to be living such a radiant life that it prompts the question, 'Why are you the way you are?' and opens the way for a positive answer of what God has done. There's nothing more silly than the answer to an unasked question. That's witnessing of the lowest order. But there's nothing more powerful and contagious than the answer to a sincere question about the source of our quality of life. That's witnessing of the highest order."[1]

Our life and actions are our greatest witness. **We must earn the right to be heard, and then speak the truths of Jesus Christ.**

What did Jesus tell Peter and Andrew in Matthew 4:18-20? The fishing illustration is perfect for witnessing. When you fish you must put bait on the hook, and wait. As a Christian, your life is the bait that will arouse curiosity. Seldom do you catch fish by harpooning them or waiting for the fish to jump out of the water onto your lap. Get the message?

Here are four thought-provoking questions for you to answer.

1. What if everyone in the world were like you in personality and attitude?

2. How would you like to reproduce what has happened to your faith in the lives of others?

3. Would you like everyone to discover what you have found?

4. If you were arrested for being a Christian, would there be enough evidence to convict you?

What do you think of Paul's attitude in Philippians 3:17—4:9, and I Corinthians 4:16?

Paul never said he was perfect (see Romans 7), yet he had enough confidence in his lifestyle that he felt his life could help point people to Jesus Christ.

Read Paul's thrilling testimony before King Agrippa and the Governor (Acts 26).

What points stand out in your mind about Paul's testimony?

Reread Acts 26:24-29. This is where the conversation gets pretty intense. What are your feelings about Paul's statement to the king in verses 28,29?

_____ Right on, Paul!

_____ Sounds boastful to me.

_____ I would be afraid to say such things.

_____ Let me at them.

_____ I'm not sure I understand.

_____ _____

Let's take a look at the source of love (which is also the source of a Christian's witness).
Read I John 4:7-21.

Why are we to love one another, according to v. 7?

What does v. 8 tell us about God?

How did God show His love to people, according to vv. 9,10?

What is the result of God's love, according to v. 11?

Why do we love, according to v. 19?

Love is the key to effective witnessing. Who can resist genuine, compassionate, unconditional love?

So let's get serious about loving others.

Who is on your "love list"?
List the names of those to whom you hope to show the love of God.

NAME   *WHAT DO YOU PLAN TO DO, AND WHEN WILL YOU BEGIN?*

_____   _____

_____   _____

_____   _____

Footnote
1. Lloyd Ogilvie, *A Life Full of Surprises* (Nashville: Abingdon Press, 1976), pp. 65,66.

10. Developing a Disciplined Devotional Life

One of the most difficult tasks in living the Christian life is that of developing a disciplined daily devotional life. Yet this is a must for spiritual growth and victory in Christ.

This section will help you understand the importance of a disciplined devotional life and challenge you to take a serious look at your priorities.

Memory Verse:

> "Discipline yourself for the
> purpose of godliness"
> **I Timothy 4:7b** *(NASB)*

After a very busy, and most likely exhausting, day in Capernaum, what did Jesus do the following day, according to Mark 1:35?

Read Joshua 1:8. (This would be a good memory verse also!)
Summarize this verse in your own words.

What is the formula for a prosperous and successful life?

Note that prosperity does not necessarily mean financial wealth. It is much closer to meaning a fulfilled and abundant life.

A disciplined daily devotional life is not an option for spiritual growth, **it is a must!** For you to grow spiritually you must pray daily, read your Bible daily and fellowship with other Christians regularly.

How would you rate your devotional life right now?

_____ Hoping to get started soon.

_____ Up and down.

_____ Boring.

_____ Getting better.

_____ Going strong.

_____ What devotional life?

_____ Really hard to remain disciplined.

_____ _____

Here are a few devotional suggestions for the beginner.

Your quiet time should occur *daily.* Consistent communication with God is important for continued growth. Quantity of time is not as important as quality. Since you call him Lord, He is your master: and that means you need to communicate with Him every day.

Your quiet time should include: Prayer, praise, thanksgiving, confession, petition, listening and Bible reading.

Praise: God loves to hear the praises of His children. "Let everything that has breath praise the Lord" (Psalm 150:6, *NASB*). Tell Him of His greatness and His majestic power. Brag on Him and adore the Lord of Lords and King of Kings.

Thanksgiving: This is another important part of prayer. "For everything give thanks, for this is God's will for you in Christ Jesus" (I Thess. 5:18, *NASB*). No matter what your situation or what major problem you are facing, there is much to be thankful for in your life. Thankfulness can help overcome negative and depressive emotions.

Confession: "If we confess our sins, he is faithful and just to forgive us our sins, and to cleanse us from all unrighteousness" (I John 1:9, *KJV*). The way to keep your communication with God clear is to confess your sins to Him. The word *confession* comes from a root word meaning to "agree together with." When you confess your sins to God you are simply agreeing with Him that you've missed the mark, and letting Him know that you desire a right relationship with Him.

43

Petition: "Ask, and it shall be given to you; seek, and you shall find; knock, and it shall be opened to you" (Matt. 7:7, *NASB*). This is an important part of your prayer life, but not the *only* part. Often people rush into the presence of God and only ask for things, then rush out of His presence. Petition includes prayers for family, friends, church, government and yourself. God is your heavenly Father, and He wants the best for you. Do not be afraid to ask, but remember who is the Lord in the relationship. (God is, not you.)

Listening: Proverbs 2:1-5. Prayer is two-way communication. When praying, take time to listen. Write down thoughts that come into your mind, then test those thoughts through the inner witness of your spirit. God is speaking to you. Take time to be quiet before the Lord.

Bible reading: "All flesh is like grass, and all its glory like the flower of grass. The grass withers, and the flower falls off, but the word of the Lord abides forever" (I Peter 1:24,25, *NASB*). Nearly everything in our world will disappear but the Word of God will abide forever. The Word of God teaches us about God, His history and His will for us today. It is of great importance to place the Word of God in your heart during your devotional time. "I have hidden your word in my heart that I might not sin against you" (Psalm 119:11, *NIV*).

Few Christians would disagree with the fact that a daily devotional life is very important for our growth in Christ, yet most Christians feel defeated in this area. In this section we want to challenge you to set specific goals for your devotional life.

1. Where is a quiet place where you can meet with God every day?

2. What time do you plan to have your quiet time with God?

3. What do you plan to do during your quiet time? (For example, read the New Testament every day and keep a prayer diary.) Be specific!

4. What are your goals for your special time with God? (In other words, what do you want to have happen during your time with God?)

Let's take a few minutes to have an actual devotional time with God.

Praise: Why are you praising God today?

Thanksgiving: List some reasons for being thankful today.

Confession: What do you need to confess (agree with God about) today?

Petition: What are your requests for God?

Listening: In the quietness of your soul, is God speaking to you through His inner witness of the Spirit?

Bible reading: What portion of Scripture did you read?

What is significant to you in this section of Scripture?

11. Handling Peer Pressure

When you become a Christian a battle begins to take place. It's a battle between your flesh (the worldly desires that still influence you) and your Spirit (God's Holy Spirit who dwells within you). One of the most difficult battles is the one against *peer pressure.*

Peer pressure is one of the most dominant influences in our lives. The effects of peer pressure can cause the five-year-old to scream a "dirty word" to impress a friend, the sixteen-year-old to get drunk at a party, and the business executive to cheat on a business deal because "everyone else does."

At times the battle between the spirit and the flesh is an all-out war. Paul describes his personal battle this way:

I don't understand myself at all, for I really want to do what is right, but I can't. I do what I don't want to—what I hate. I know perfectly well that what I am doing is wrong, and my bad conscience proves that I agree with these laws I am breaking. But I can't help myself, because I'm no longer doing it. It is sin inside me that is stronger than I am that makes me do these evil things.

I know I am rotten through and through so far as my old sinful nature is concerned. No matter which way I turn I can't make myself do right. I want to but I can't. When I want to do good, I don't; and when I try not to do wrong, I do it anyway. Now if I am doing what I don't want to do, it is plain where the trouble is: sin still has me in its evil grasp.

It seems to be a fact of life that when I want to do what is right, I inevitably do what is wrong. I love to do God's will so far as my new nature is concerned; but there is something else deep within me, in my lower nature, that is at war with my mind and wins the fight and makes me a slave to the sin that is still within me. In my mind I want to be God's willing servant but instead I find myself still enslaved to sin.

So you see how it is: my new life tells me to do right, but the old nature that is still inside me loves to sin. Oh, what a terrible predicament I'm in! Who will free me from my slavery to this deadly lower nature? Thank God! It has been done by Jesus Christ our Lord. He has set me free.

Romans 7:15-25 (*TLB*)

Can you identify with Paul?

In what areas of your life do you find your hardest battle?

What do you think Paul means in Romans 7:24,25?

Since peer pressure is such a battle in our lives it is important to fight the battle with the needed ammunition to help win the war.

Below are listed four types of ammunition that will help you win the battle.

1) Everyone you spend time with has an influence on you.

2) Choose your friends wisely.

3) Remember your uniqueness. You're special in God's eyes!

4) Seek first the kingdom of God.

1. **Everyone you spend time with has an influence on you. People influence you either positively or negatively. Perhaps a few have a neutral influence on you.**

Who are the people who have a positive influence on your life?

What traits in their lives would you like to acquire more of?

Who are the people who have a negative influence on your life? (You might want to list only their initials.)

What traits in their lives do you not want to acquire?

2. Choose your friends wisely.

As you can see from the first bit of "ammunition" for fighting peer pressure, peers can and do have a positive effect on us as well as a negative effect. It's a fact that you become like the people you spend time with. It's important to choose the people you would like to become friends with. Remember, it takes time to develop meaningful friendships.

With whom would you like to develop a better positive friendship in the coming months?

What will you do to develop that friendship?

As a Christian it is important to choose both Christian and non-Christian friends. We need non-Christian friends in order to be a witness and to keep in touch with "the world." We need Christian friends in order to be influenced in a positive way, and to have fellow believers with whom to share our joys, doubts and frustrations within the faith.

Not only is it important to choose our friends wisely, it is very important to make sure we have proper fellowship.

Do you have good fellowship with other Christians?

Do you feel comfortable sharing your hurts and joys within this fellowship?

Take the advice of the writer of the book of Hebrews seriously.

> In response to all he has done for us, let us outdo each other in being helpful and kind to each other and in doing good.
>
> Let us not neglect our church meetings, as some people do, but encourage and warn each other, especially now that the day of his coming back again is drawing near.
> **Hebrews 10:24,25 (TLB)**

3. Remember your uniqueness. You are special in God's eyes!

Try this experiment some day. Go somewhere in your city or town, and take some time to people-watch. Observe carefully what people are wearing, what they are saying, the music they listen to, and so on. You'll find out that most people, when it gets right down to it, are trying to be just like everyone else.

Have you ever wished you could look like Bill or Susie or wear clothes just like Mary or Tom? Of course you have! At times we all wish we could be like someone else. Yet when we take God seriously we learn that He created us to be unique and special. Because He made us we do not have to impress others by outside appearances. We are set free to be the men and women God desires us to be. We are free from the need to compromise our values in order to be accepted by our peers. If we really think about it, we will be more accepted by our peers when they observe a confidence in ourselves that God gives us as we grow in Him.

List a few of your own special and unique qualities.

In the space below, write a thank-you note to God, thanking Him for your uniqueness and special qualities in your life.

4. Seek first the kingdom of God.

> But seek first His kingdom, and His righteousness; and all these things shall be added to you.
>
> Matthew 6:33 *(NASB)*

This advice from the lips of Jesus is probably the very best advice you could receive in dealing with peer pressure.

Read Matthew 6:25-34.

What is the advice of Jesus concerning what we eat, drink or wear?

How does this advice apply to our battle with peer pressure?

Jesus gave some other advice that is very much worth repeating: "No one can serve two masters; for either he will hate the one and love the other, or he will hold to one and despise the other. You cannot serve God and mammon" (Matt. 6:24, *NASB*).

In other words, in this battle we are fighting between our spirit and our flesh, there is always a winner. Compromise and giving in to peer pressure is always a victory for the flesh. Putting God first is always a victory for the spirit.

12. What Is God's Will for My Life?

It seems as though any book on how to know the will of God sells rapidly, and any talk or seminar on God's will is well attended. Why? The answer is easy. Everyone wants to know just what God has in store for his or her life. Who hasn't thought of questions such as, "Who will I marry?" "What career should I pursue?" "Should I get another degree?" And the list goes on and on. When we read these books and attend the seminars we are often looking for an "easy answer." Let's get the facts straight: *There are no simple answers or easy formulas for knowing the will of God.*

There are, however, some very helpful suggestions for finding out the will of God for our lives.

1. You are living out the will of God today.

We often miss the boat because we are always saying, "When I get out of school I'll find out the will of God," or, "When I find the right person to marry, then I'll know the will of God." Yet we miss the fact that as Christians today we are living out the will of God. You are a kingdom person today! Don't have your mind so set on the future that you miss doing the will of God *today.*

The advice of Jesus in the sermon on the mount is the best possible advice you could receive.

> **"So don't be anxious about tomorrow. God will
> take care of your tomorrow too. *Live one day at a time!*
> (Matt. 6:34, *TLB*, emphasis added.)**

How does this verse apply to you today?

What do you think is God's will for you today?

2. We can know the will of God through the Bible.

> **"Thy word is a lamp unto my feet
> and a light unto my path"
> (Psalm 119:105, *KJV*)**

The Bible is our authority when it comes to knowing God's will. As we read and study the Bible we can know how God wants us to live in many situations.

Look up the following verses and match them to the word or phrase found in the Bible that is God's will for our lives.

Love the Lord your God with all your heart, mind and soul.　　　　James 1:26

Be thankful in all situations.　　　　Matthew 6:33

Do not be conformed to this world.　　　　Exodus 20:12

Seek first God's Kingdom.　　　　Exodus 20:14,15

Bridle your tongue.　　　　I Corinthians 6:19,20

Do not steal or commit adultery.　　　　I Thessalonians 5:18

Honor your father and mother.　　　　Romans 12:1,2

Glorify God with your body.　　　　Matthew 22:37

This list could go on and on. However, the Bible does not deal with every situation. For example, nowhere in Scripture will you find what college you should attend, or whether you should drive a VW or a Chevrolet. When the Scripture is silent on a subject, we look at other situations to find out the will of God for our lives.

3. Seek the advice and counsel of others whom you respect.

We all need to take the advice of the writer of Proverbs seriously

"Make plans by seeking advice . . ."
(Prov. 20:18, *NIV*).

"Where there is no guidance the people fall; but in abundance of counselors there is victory" (Prov. 11:14, *NASB*).

Who can you go to for good, solid, sound advice?

You need people in your life, perhaps in your family or at your church, to whom you can go for advice and counsel. Weigh their thoughts heavily, but remember, you must ultimately make your own decisions.

4. Prayer is another way of knowing the will of God.

Paul gave strong advice to his friends in the Philippian church when he wrote:

"Don't worry about anything; instead, pray about everything; tell God your needs and don't forget to thank him for his answers"
(Phil. 4:6, *TLB*)

What does Paul suggest to do instead of worrying about God's will?

Now look up Philippians 4:7.
Write down the result of following Paul's instructions in the previous verse.

What are some specific areas in your life that you should be praying about?

5. At times, we can know the will of God through circumstances.

   Some people call it the open-door/closed-door policy of knowing circumstances. Be careful to look at events and situations over which you have no control as possible actions from God. Watch them carefully and slowly. Don't act impulsively on circumstances. Use the other methods of prayer, Bible reading and the wise counsel of others to help you see if the circumstances are from God.

   What are a couple of circumstances over which you had no control that you feel God used to lead you to do His will?

   Look up Romans 12:1,2 and tell why you think those verses are important for any study on the will of God.